Lets read with
Pull and Learn
PHONICS
Cub in a Tub
Written by Sue Graves
Illustrated by
Gustavo Mazali
D1283387

Gus the cub
was playing in
the sun.

"Phew! I'm so hot," said Gus.

some cold water
in a mug.

Then, she picked up an old tin tub.

She filled the
tub with water
using a big jug.

"Be careful Gus!"

"Be careful Gus,"
said Mom, "don't
splash the bug!"

“This is great fun,” said Gus. “Now I’m a really cool cub!”

"I am a cool cub!"

book-studio

This edition published 2005
The Book Studio
Henson Way, Kettering, NN16 8PX

Manufactured in China